MW00623805

How Do I Know You?

Dementia at the End of Life

Dementia isn't a specific disease. Instead, dementia describes a group of symptoms affecting memory, thinking and social abilities severely enough to interfere with daily functioning. Alzheimer's disease is the most common cause of progressive dementia in older adults, but there are a number of causes of dementia.

— The Mayo Clinic

This booklet is a guide to addressing the challenges that are present in the weeks to days before a person with dementia dies. It is just a sketch, a loose drawing of symptoms, problems, and possible solutions. It isn't chiseled in stone - every person suffers dementia in their own way. In fact, there are so many different degrees of dementia that it is hard to make general statements about its progression. The information given here will apply to some and not to others. Use this booklet simply as a source of ideas to think about.

As you read through this booklet remember I am talking about anyone experiencing the symptoms of dementia no matter the clinical name for their diagnosis. I am going to use the word "dementia" to represent all the diseases that have dementia as a symptom.

It is very important to remember that most of the information in this booklet does not apply to people with dementia who are eating well. It is only when a person is not eating, or eating very little, that the dying process generally begins.

The Long Goodbye

Alzheimer's disease is sometimes called "the long goodbye." From diagnosis to death is generally a very long time, most often years. Those years are filled with watching a loved one gradually become less and less able to function in the world. Most diseases that include dementia result in a "long goodbye."

It is hard to watch someone you care about lose the ability to live what we consider a normal life. To know that they are unable to do the things that we think living is about - eating, being active, finding humor, interacting, remembering - leaves us feeling frustrated and helpless. What becomes their normal behavior goes against everything we feel is normal about living.

Living with someone who has dementia is a daily challenge. It is a constant reminder that this person is not who they once were. It presents the difficulty of learning how to live with the person that they have become.

Our instincts tell us our loved one needs to eat and move to live. So that is what we tend to focus on because it feels both necessary and normal to us. Will forcing them to eat and get out of bed lengthen their life? Probably. But if life were different, and you were the one with dementia wanting to not eat and stay in bed, what course of action would you choose for yourself? Would you rather have your final days filled with pressure, force, and conflict or would you rather go peacefully to sleep a bit sooner?

It is hard to comprehend what is going on in the mind of a person with dementia. We can only ask ourselves what we would want if the tables were turned.

It is important to mention the hostility, anger, and aggression that can occur with dementia. These facets of a changing personality can hurt and bewilder us. I can only suggest that you gently remind yourself not to take these effects of your loved one's disease personally (which is of course much easier said than done) and to try to continually separate the current behavior from the memory of the relationship. Try to love the person and the memory even if you have trouble with the current behavior.

Continuous Grief

For anyone with a life threatening illness there is a gradual progression from diagnosis to death. With all terminal illness grief begins with diagnosis - but it is an anticipatory grief. Unconsciously we all know we are going to die, but a patient who has received a terminal diagnosis has a timeline. They have been told roughly when they are going to die, so the patient and their loved ones anticipate the need to grieve. But the real work of grieving begins after the patient has died.

When someone we love has dementia, because the mind fades before the body dies, our grief is continuous from diagnosis to death. We grieve for each shared memory that we lose. We grieve for each ability, each experience, each interaction that is no longer forthcoming. We have losses everyday.

Our loved one gradually becomes a person we don't really know. With that comes not knowing how to interact with them. "Who is this woman who is my mother? I don't know her and she doesn't know me. What do we do with each other?" As the person gradually changes and becomes less able to function mentally and emotionally, WE must adjust. The person with dementia can't even fathom what is occurring.

We must learn to accept our loved one not for who they used to be, but for who they are now. This is part of our grieving.

Memories are made of the past, and hopes are part

of the future. People with dementia force those around them to live in the present - to see that what is happening right now is what is important. With memory loss the past is gone and the future is not contemplated; only the present has value.

Grief for the dead is self-centered. Most of us believe the deceased is in a better place, so our grief is about us. We have to adjust to what we have lost. Grief for a person with dementia is for the afflicted as well as for ourselves. We grieve for them as we see that they are unaware of the changes in their perceptions. We grieve that they often don't know what they have lost. We grieve for the change in their relationship with us.

Grief for the dead allows us to move forward, to make a new life built on positive, balanced memories. Grief for a person with dementia holds us in place, prevents us from moving on and rebuilding. Everyday we are reminded, just by being in their presence, of what we have lost and are still losing.

My remedy for the continuous grief experienced by the family of a person with dementia is acceptance and giving. Acceptance for who the person has become and what they can do today. Acceptance that they are unable to consciously give us what we want from them, as a spouse, as a child, as a sibling, or as a friend. Acceptance that our life has changed forever.

However, we can give to them. We can give love, we can give attendance, and we can give patience. We can ask for nothing, just give and see what happens. We also need to give the same love, patience, and acceptance to ourselves as we go through this challenging experience of continuous grief.

Having a loved one with dementia is "the long goodbye." We lose the person we know long before their body dies. This means we are grieving continuously whether we are aware of that grief or not.

Hard Choices: Food, Water, and Artificial Feeding

A person with dementia does not necessarily exhibit the signs of approaching death like someone with cancer or heart disease. The timeline is off. Where a person with a life threatening illness enters the dying process two to four months before death actually occurs, there are no such points of reference to guide us with dementia. In a non-dementia related disease, eating gradually decreases, sleeping increases, and the person withdraws inward from the activity of living as they approach death. With dementia, those same behaviors may have no relation to the dying process. It is not until eating becomes a big problem (which can include not chewing, not swallowing, and choking), that we can consider a person with dementia as having begun to die.

If we don't eat, we don't live. When a person is consistently not eating, a difficult decision needs to be made. Do you have a physician perform the surgical procedure called a gastrostomy? An operation that puts a tube directly into the stomach and sews it in place, a gastrostomy allows liquid nourishment to be given daily, often at night while the person is sleeping.

There are many feelings and opinions about the artificial feeding question. I hope that the person diagnosed with the disease that produced dementia created an Advance Directive while they were still able to make rational decisions. In it they should have outlined what they would like done when they are no longer eating. A lot of anguish is avoided when an Advance Directive is in place.

If there is no Advance Directive the family is faced with the artificial feeding decision. Do you let life as the person has come to live it ebb away or do you medically intervene and feed the body?

First, we need to understand that any life

threatening disease will progress regardless of whether or not the person eats. With that hard truth in mind, here are some things to think about that may help you make your decision. The natural way that we all die, if we are dying from disease or old age, is by gradually not eating and not drinking. By choosing to not artificially feed a person with dementia you are allowing that person to approach death in a normal way. What would you choose to do if you were making this decision for yourself? How would you want to live and die?

If artificial feeding is chosen the body and mind will continue to deteriorate, but at a slower pace. Eventually, in spite of the nourishment, the body will die. Watch for the signs that signify that it will be weeks to days before death that are described later in this booklet.

If the decision is made not to artificially feed, ALWAYS, ALWAYS OFFER FOOD AND WATER. You don't just one day stop feeding someone. Generally, at this point the person is struggling against eating. We are the ones that are concerned about food intake. The person's body has already begun to shut down and is probably disliking food. OFFER, but don't plead or force. Also beware of choking.

The American Alzheimers Association and the American Geriatric Society both have research that points to the lack of benefit and often harm from artificial feeding.

On the journey toward death, as the body stops eating, it also stops drinking water. We all recognize the body's need for water. As our loved one stops drinking we tend to panic, and think they should have IV fluids (water given through a needle and tubing in the arm) to keep the body at least comfortable. However, when a person has entered the dying process their body begins shutting down and stops functioning normally. The kidneys, which process liquids, are not performing their job anymore. If we begin IV fluid, often times the fluid stays trapped in the body's cells and lungs. This causes increased discomfort and congestion, which is the opposite of what we're trying to do.

When a person has entered the dying process the body doesn't want food or water. If they are not eating any food or drinking sufficient fluid to keep them hydrated they are days to a week from death. When this happens the calcium in their blood will begin to rise because of the dehydration (not enough water in the body to operate efficiently). When the calcium gets high enough a person goes to sleep and doesn't wake up. If left to its own devices the body gives itself comfort and life ends in sleep. This is the normal, natural way we die.

Regardless of whether or not you have decided to artificially feed, once a person enters the dying process death will probably come within weeks to days. How long this takes will depend upon their weight and how much they are eating and drinking. Now you will see all the signs of approaching death that occur from other diseases and old age. Those signs will fit into the normal timeline that affects others as death approaches.

Now It's Truly Goodbye: One to Three Weeks Before Death

Weeks before death a person's breathing changes. It often becomes rapid with congestion, or very slow with mouth gaping movements. Their blood pressure lowers, the coloring of their hands and feet becomes bluish or dark. They sleep with their eyes partially open and are often restless, picking at their clothes, bed linens, and the air. In the hours to minutes before death most people are non-responsive. They may be talking and moving, but they don't respond to what is happening around them or even to touch. We generally sleep through our final experience. (Read my booklet *Gone From My Sight, The Dying Experience* for more detailed information).

We, the watchers, often get very confused about the moment someone takes their last breath. We let our own fear of the moment distort our perception of what is happening. Say your goodbyes, talk, hug, interact as though your loved one hears and understands you even if they have not responded or understood you for months or years. Say what is in your heart, express your love and gratitude for sharing their life with you. Bless them on their journey.

Living in the "long goodbye" is challenging at its best, and tiring, frustrating, sad, and heartbreaking the rest of the time. As the end approaches, as family and significant others, you will experience deep sadness. In that sadness will hide a sense of relief (with its ensuing guilt). Be gentle with yourselves, know that you always did the best you could in an extremely difficult and demanding time. Hold on to the good and gently let go of all else.

Those we love don't go away,
They walk beside us every day —
unseen,
unheard,
but always near,
still loved,
still missed
and
very dear.

— Author Unknown —

Summary

Dementia doesn't fit the guidelines for signs of approaching death from disease or old age

The challenge of learning how to live with the person you are losing:

- The past is a memory, the future is a hope, it's the present that is NOW
- Make today special
- Live a new normal

Grieving begins with diagnosis

When addressing hostility, anger, and aggression separate the current behavior from the memory of your relationship

Don't take aggression and hostility personally; it is the result of the disease not the person

When not eating, difficulty swallowing, and/or choking becomes an issue artificial feeding becomes an option:

- There are no right or wrong choices, just difficult choices

If artificial feeding is chosen:

- Decline will continue
- Dementia will progress
- Death will be forestalled for an undetermined amount of time

If artificial feeding is not chosen:

- Signs of approaching death will begin depending upon:
    - Body weight, how much the person is eating
    - General body condition
- ALWAYS OFFER FOOD AND WATER, just don't force

Signs of approaching death that signal weeks:

- Breathing changes; becomes rapid or starts and stops, puffing sounds
- Sleeps with eyes partially open
- Restlessness, picking at bed clothes and the air

Signs of approaching death that signal days:

- The coloring of hands and feet becomes bluish or dark
- Blood pressure lowers
- Congestion

Signs of approaching death that signal hours:

- Most people are non-responsive
- Breathing changes to look like a fish breathing

Say goodbye, hug, and interact as though the person can understand you

Resources

- www.alz.org; Alzheimers Association; help line: 1-800-272-3900

- www.Alzheimerslocator.com; provides guide to local resources: 844-251-8621

- www.alzheimers.gov; caregiver resources

- https://www.ncbi.nlm.nih.gov/pmc/articles/PMC5102197/; from the US National Library of Medicine

- https://onlinelibrary.wiley.com/doi/pdf/10.1111/jgs.12924; American Geriatrics Society

- ALZ.org/media/documents/feeding-issues-statement.pdf

- www.nia.nih.gov; National Institute on Aging

- www.bkbooks.com; Barbara Karnes, RN; end of life education materials: 360-828-7132

Notes

BARBARA KARNES RN
end of life education materials

www.bkbooks.com • bkbooks@bkbooks.com

ORDER FORM

CONTACT NAME: _____

ORGANIZATION: _____

STREET: _____

CITY: _____ STATE: _____ ZIP: _____

PHONE: _____ FAX_____

EMAIL: _____

❏ NEW ORDER   ❏ REORDER   PO# : _____

BILLING ADDRESS: (IF DIFFERENT FROM ABOVE)

BILLING CONTACT / ORGANIZATION: _____

STREET: _____

CITY: _____ STATE: _____ ZIP: _____

PAYMENT:

❏ INVOICE US (AGENCIES ONLY - Net 30 days)

❏ CHECK ENCLOSED (Payable to B. Karnes Books)

❏ CREDIT CARD (enter card information below)

NAME ON CARD: _____

CREDIT CARD #: | _____ | | _____ | | _____ | | _____ |

EXP DATE: _____ CVV CODE:_____

Barbara Karnes Books
MAIL TO: PO Box 822139 • Vancouver, WA 98682
Phone (9-4 pm PST) 360-828-7132 • Fax 360-828-7142

PRODUCT TITLE (See Catalog)	LANGUAGE	QTY	$ PER UNIT (See Chart Below)	SUBTOT

TOTAL	$
POSTAGE (See Chart Below)	$
SALES TAX (We Collect for Only These States: GA, IL, IN, KS, MI, MN, NC, OH, VA and WA)	$
GRAND TOTAL FOR ORDER (add together Total, Postage, Sales Tax)	$

Pricing & Discounts for Booklets
1 – 9 ....$3.00 per copy
10 - 99 ....$2.00 per copy
100 – 249 ....$1.80 per copy
250 - 499 ....$1.70 per copy
500 - 999 ....$1.60 per copy
1,000 - 2,499 ....$1.50 per copy
2,500 - 4,999 ....$1.40 per copy
5,000 - 9,999 ....$1.30 per copy
10,000 - 24,999 .....$1.20 per copy

Call for Priority Shipping rates. Quantity discounts are applied to individual products. Postage may be adjusted for rate increases. Visit **www.bkbooks.com** for discounts, postage rates not listed, secure credit card orders, new materials, and eBooks. All fees are subject to change without notice.

Postage & Handling
1 copy $3.0
2 copies $4.0
3 – 9 copies $5.0
10 – 25 copies $6.0
26 – 50 copies $8.0
51 – 100 copies $10.0
101 – 250 copies $18.0
251 – 300 copies $25.0
301 – 500 copies $35.0

Barbara Karnes Books
MAIL TO: PO Box 822139 • Vancouver, WA 98682
Phone (9-4 pm PST) 360-828-7132 • Fax 360-828-7142